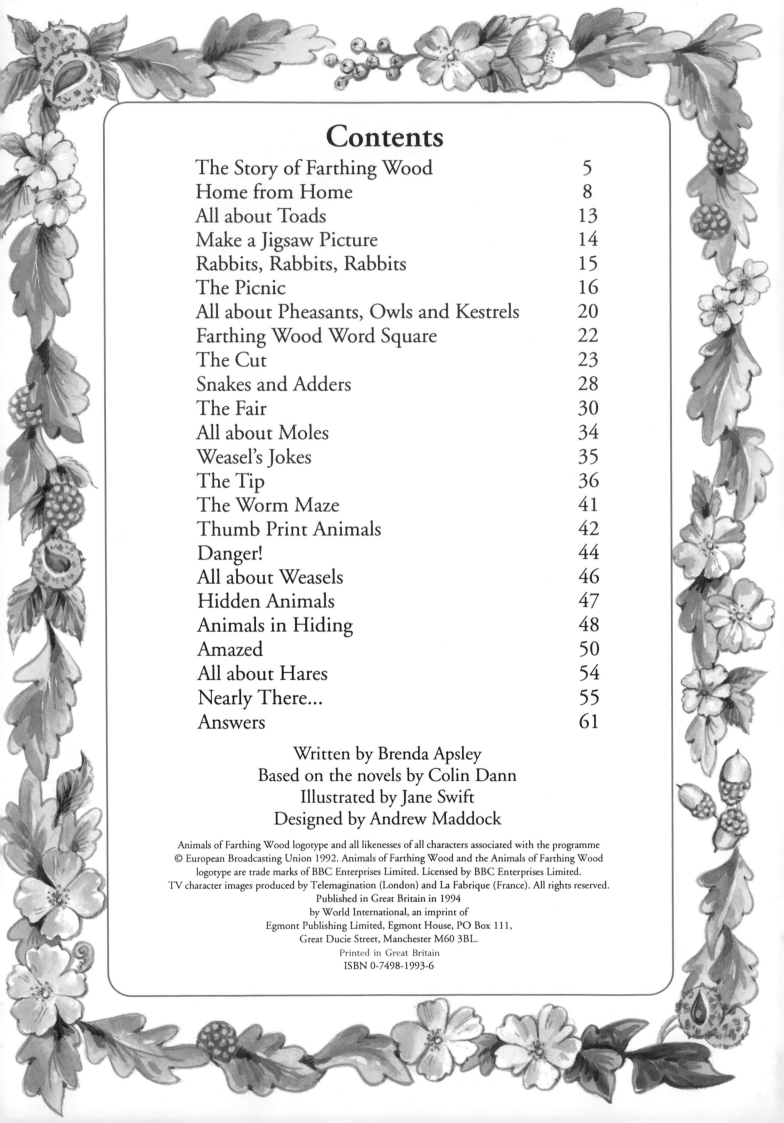

Contents

Written by Brenda Apsley
Based on the novels by Colin Dann
Illustrated by Jane Swift
Designed by Andrew Maddock

Published in Great Britain in 1994
by World International, an imprint of
Egmont Publishing Limited, Egmont House, PO Box 111,
Great Ducie Street, Manchester M60 3BL.
Printed in Great Britain
ISBN 0-7498-1993-6

The Story of Farthing Wood

Farthing Wood used to be a good place to live. The animals there had homes to live in, food to eat and water to drink.

But that was before the humans arrived. They took over Farthing Heath bit by bit, building roads and houses, and now they were moving in on the wood itself, cutting down trees and clearing the places where the animals lived.

When the humans filled in the pond they destroyed the animals' water supply. And without water to drink the animals were in real danger. Something had to be done.

A general meeting was called, and all the animals of Farthing Wood came, from the smallest shrew to wise old Badger.

"We cannot stay here without water to drink," said Badger.

Fox agreed. "But where can we go?" he asked.

No one knew – until Toad arrived. He had been taken away in a jam jar and it had taken him many months to travel back, only to find that his pond had been filled in.

"Did you see any safe places to live on your travels?" Badger asked him.

"I did, mateys," said Toad, "I did. A nature reserve called White Deer Park. We could all live in safety there."

The animals all agreed that they would leave the wood that very night. Toad would guide them and Fox would be their leader.

"We must agree not to harm each other," said Badger. "Even natural enemies like Adder and the Fieldmice."

The animals all held up a paw, claw or wing, and swore the Oath of Mutual Protection. "We promise not to frighten, bully or eat each other on the long journey ahead."

That night the animals of Farthing Wood met at the edge of the trees and set off on their great adventure.

Home from Home

One dark night, Owl flew back to the animals. "Lots of trees ahead of yoooooo," she said. "A sign says PARK. Is it White Deer Park, Toad?"

"No, mateys," said Toad. "White Deer Park is many days of hard travelling from here."

"What is it, then?" asked Mole.

"It's a place where humans go to walk and play with their dogs," said Toad.

"Dogs?" said Adder, alarmed.

"Humans?" said Badger. "Will it be safe?"

Toad nodded. "Look, here we are. The gates are closed for the night. There won't be any humans or dogs inside tonight."

The animals squeezed under the gates.

Fox sniffed. His nose twitched and he followed the scent to a litter bin. Cartons and wrappers and bottles spilt out on to the ground. Fox found half a burger and a hot dog sausage. There were dried-up sandwiches, too.

A little further on the animals came to some netting. "There'sss sssomething moving in there," said Adder, whose keen eyes didn't miss much.

"It's a rabbit," said Mrs Rabbit.

"Not like you, though," said Adder. "It'sss white with black ssspotsss. And it'sss fatter."

Toad knew all about it. "It's what them there humans calls a tame rabbit. Lives here in this big cage. They calls it Pets' Corner."

The tame rabbit heard them and hopped over. "It's an easy life here. There's lots to eat and," she said, looking at Adder and Fox, "there's no one trying to eat us. Want to come inside? Slip under the fence behind that bush. There's a gap."

The little animals went inside and nibbled carrots and cabbage leaves. They were still eating when the sun started to peep over the trees. "Come on," said Fox. "We have to find somewhere safe to spend the day."

"Try the Model Village," said the tame rabbit, pointing.

In the Model Village the animals found tiny houses, shops and a church. "It's just the right size for us!" squeaked the Shrews.

"Yes, I think we should stay here," said a Fieldmouse. "Food, water, and these lovely little houses to live in. It's just the perfect place to live."

"It's too close to the humans," Badger warned, but the Fieldmice shook their heads.

"Badger's right," said Fox. "We must stay together."

The sky was getting lighter and lighter. "The humans will be here soon," warned Vixen.

"We must hide," said Fox. "We'll all meet at the gates at nightfall and travel on." He looked at the Shrews. "All of us."

The bigger animals hid in deep hedges and shrubs while the Fieldmice, Voles and Shrews settled down to sleep in the Model Village.

But not for long…

"What's that?" said Mrs Fieldmouse, suddenly wide awake. She could hear loud human voices – and they were very close. She crept to the window and looked out at a forest of moving legs. It was a group of small children on a school trip. They shouted and called out. "We'll never get any sleep here," said Mrs Fieldmouse.

In the village bakery the Voles were asleep on the counter when one of them was prodded awake. She leapt up as a little fat finger poked through the window and wiggled around. "Oh, help!" she whispered.

The Shrews were in the church. The chattering and giggling had woken them, too. "Look, over there!" said one of them as they hid behind the tiny wooden pews. A huge eye appeared in the church door as one of the children peered inside.

"I'm scared," said one.

"So am I," said another. "This is a horrible, dangerous place. I don't like it."

"Shhh," said the oldest Shrew. "They'll go away soon, I'm sure."

They did, but other humans arrived. All day long feet clattered by, and the animals heard loud, scary voices. The animals didn't dare go to sleep.

At last, at the end of the afternoon, things were quiet again. The animals relaxed a little and started to settle down to sleep.

Suddenly they heard a loud whooshing, sloshing sound.

10

One of the Voles peeped out. "Look out!" he cried as loudly as he could. "It's a flood. The main street is full of water, and it's coming this way!"

The Voles jumped up on to the high shelves as bubbly, soapy water rushed in, wetting the ends of their tails.

It wasn't a flood – the man who looked after the Model Village was washing the streets with soapy water and a big brush.

After a few scary minutes the water ran out of the houses again. The little animals crept outside one by one. It was dusk, and the man had gone home.

At nightfall the animals of Farthing Wood all met at the park gates. Fox checked that everyone was there.

"Do you think the Shrews, Fieldmice and Voles will come with us?" asked Badger.

"I don't know," said Fox.

They were about to set off when the little animals scurried up. "Ssso you're coming with usss?" hissed Adder.

A Fieldmouse yawned. "Yes please. That Model Village wasn't a safe home for us after all. You were right, Badger, we must all stay together until we get to White Deer Park."

All about Toads

Toads are bigger and fatter than frogs and have dry, warty skin. It is greeny-brown and mottled, which means their enemies cannot see them in damp leaves. They walk slowly, but can leap if there is danger.

Toads live in water when they are young, and eat water plants. They live on land when they grow up, and eat insects. They like damp, dark corners under hedges and logs.

The toes on their back legs are webbed, for swimming. The fingers on their front feet are not webbed.

Toads sleep right through the winter, and in spring go back to the pond where they were hatched to raise more babies. The female lays about 2,000 eggs in a string of jelly. Tiny tadpoles grow from the eggs. After about 3 weeks the toadlets can swim. When they grow front legs and lose their tails they leave the pond to live on land.

Make a Jigsaw Picture

1 Draw a Farthing Wood picture like this one.
Colour it using crayons, pencils or felt-tips.

2 Glue the picture to a piece of card (a cereal box will do).

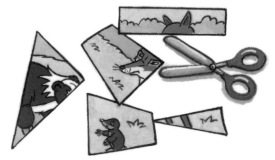

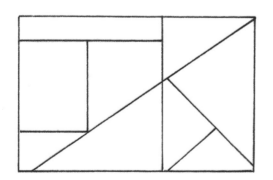

3 On the back of the card, draw some lines.

4 Cut out the lines so that you have lots of jigsaw pieces.
Ask a grown-up to help you.

Can you put the picture back together again?

14

Rabbits, Rabbits, Rabbits

Can you find the two baby rabbits who are exactly the same?

The answer is on page 61.

The Picnic

The animals were resting on the edge of a wood one day when Mole's pointy snout started to twitch. "Mmm," he said. "I smell food."

Mole followed the scent with his snout and looked out of the bushes. Some humans were having a picnic on the grass.

Mole was just about to walk out of the bushes when Badger stopped him. "You know better than to go near humans," he said.

Badger led Mole back into the wood. Badger was soon fast asleep again. But Mole was very much awake. And his snout was still twitching.

He crept to the edge of the wood again, and looked this way and that. The humans were nowhere to be seen. But the picnic was still on the grass.

Mole scurried across the grass. Soon he was eating greedily. There were little sausage rolls and ham sandwiches, pies and crisps.

Mole was so busy eating that he didn't hear the humans coming back until it was almost too late. He hid under a paper napkin on a plate.

"It looks like rain," said one of the humans. "Let's pack up." He threw the plate, napkin – and Mole – into a dark picnic basket.

Back in the wood, Badger woke up. He looked around. "Where's Mole? Has anyone seen him?" he asked the others, but no one had.

Badger had a good idea where Mole might be. "I think Mole might be at a picnic," he told the others. "And he may be in danger. Come on."

Kestrel flew ahead. Mole was nowhere to be seen, and the humans were carrying the picnic basket back along the path to their car.

"I can't see Mole anywhere," Kestrel told the others. "He must be in that big basket the humans are carrying. I know what to do. Wait here."

Kestrel was soon back, followed by a swarm of buzzing wasps. "Don't sting the humans," she told them. "Just buzz around a bit."

The wasps flew to the humans and buzzed around them. "Wasps!" cried the humans. They dropped the picnic basket and ran to their car.

Fox put his head into the picnic basket and lifted Mole out. Badger brushed crisp crumbs from his friend's fur. "Silly, silly Mole," he said.

But Mole didn't care about the danger he had been in. "Fox, could you get that pork pie for me before we go?" he said. "It smells yummy."

All about Pheasants, Owls and Kestrels

Male pheasants are bright, with a long tail. The females are a duller brown colour with black markings.

They spend most of their time on the ground, but they can fly, and sleep in trees. They are very shy. Their cry is ko-kok, ko-kok.

Pheasants eat grasses and shoots, seeds, nuts and berries.

Females scrape a hollow on the ground for a nest and lay between 8 and 15 eggs, one each day. Their camouflage markings make it difficult to see them when they are on the nest. The young chicks are covered in soft down. They can fly when they are about 12 days old, but stay with their mother for some weeks, eating insects, then plants.

Tawny owls, like the Farthing Wood Owl, have brown feathers with darker markings. They are very hard to spot when they sleep during the day, leaning against tree bark.

They hunt at night. Their eyes are on the front of their heads, which they can turn right round so that they can see in all directions. They have very good eyesight and hearing and can fly silently.

They catch prey in strong claws with sharp talons on the end and can swallow rats and small birds whole.

The tufts on the side of the owl's head are not ears, but tufts of feathers they wiggle this way and that, signalling to each other. Their ears are on the side of their head, and can detect the sound of the tiniest creatures scurrying around.

Kestrels are expert hunters. They fly very fast and can hover high in the sky, beating their wings so fast they look almost motionless. Their big eyes are always on the lookout for the slightest movement that might mean food. If they see prey like small birds and animals they swoop down, snatching it quickly in sharp claws called talons and tearing it with razor-sharp beaks.

Kestrels live in open country rather than forests as their wide wings make it difficult to fly through trees.

The females are red-brown with darker markings. The males have a grey head and tail. Their call is kee kee kee.

Kestrels do not build nests, but use other birds' nests, or ledges. They lay 4 to 6 eggs, and the young chicks are covered in fluffy white down before their feathers grow.

21

Farthing Wood Word Square

Can you find the names of the Farthing Wood animals in the word square? Look up, down, backwards, forwards and from corner to corner.

```
A X W T M S K M R J
Y H E D G E H O G N
V B V U H L I L Q O
I D C L E S A E W I
X R Z V K R J G H P
E E A K E S T R E L
N D U G F L D R P W
E D D F X T S A O O
W A E B C D M F O X
B G H A R E Y N Q T
```

☑ ADDER   ☑ HEDGEHOG   ☑ TOAD

☑ BADGER   ☑ KESTREL   ☑ VIXEN

☑ FOX   ☑ MOLE   ☑ WEASEL

☑ HARE   ☑ OWL

The solution is on page 61.

22

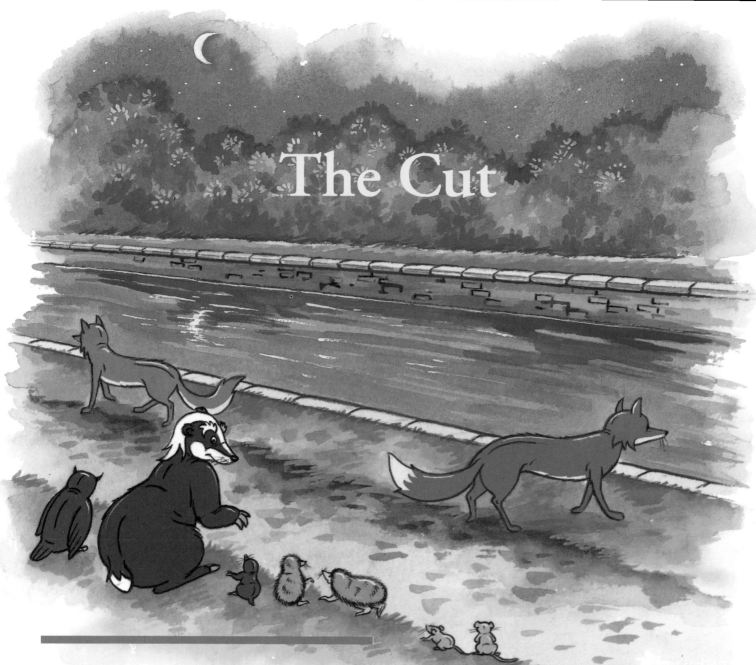

The Cut

It was a dark, dark night. The only light came from tiny stars that shone in the black sky. Owl flew on to find out what was up ahead. She could see very well in the dark. "Water ahead of yoooo," she said.

Soon the animals could see the gleam of moonlight on water themselves. They stopped and looked. Was it a stream, or a river? The water was flat, with no ripples or movement on its surface. Its banks were straight and it ran in a straight line as far as they could see.

"This isn't like any river I've seen before," said Badger.

Fox agreed. "Wait here, everyone," he said. "I'll go one way. Vixen, you go the other. See if there's a crossing place."

Mrs Hedgehog sat down heavily. "Thank goodness we can take a rest. My paws are hurting."

Mole flopped down beside her. "I don't think I can walk much further." He called to his special friend, Badger. "Hey, Badger, come over and sit with us for a while." His voice was loud in the still night.

Suddenly the animals heard a strange voice. "Hey, you lot, keep the noise down, will you? Some of us are trying to sleep."

The voice came from the water, and soon two beady black eyes appeared, and a whiskery, twitching nose.

"And who are you?" hissed Adder, eyes glinting.

"I," said the voice, "am Water Vole. And this here is my home. I was minding my own business, fast asleep, when you noisy lot came along and woke me. What's all the fuss about?"

"We're trying to find a place to cross the river," said Mole.

"What river?" asked Water Vole.

Badger pointed. "This river, where you live."

"But this isn't a river," said Water Vole. "It's a canal, a waterway that the humans made. For narrowboats and barges and things. We call it the Cut."

Just then Vixen came running up. "No crossing that way," she said.

Fox arrived a few seconds later, panting hard. "I can't find a crossing place. The river is wide all the way, too wide for some of us to swim. And deep."

"It is," said Water Vole. "But there must be a crossing place. Let me think." He didn't have to think for long. "Got it. You can cross at the lock."

Badger told Fox that the river wasn't a river at all. "It's a canal. But what is this lock thing?"

"It's the place where the boats go from one level to another, a bit like steps or stairs," Water Vole explained. "The lock has two big gates. You could run across the top of them."

"I think I saw the lock," said Vixen. "But the gates were open."

"That's the snag," said Water Vole. "You'll have to wait for some humans in a boat to come along and close them."

"So we'll have to cross in daylight?" asked Fox.

"Right."

"I don't like it," said Fox. "But what else can we do? We can't go around this canal thing, and we've got to cross it, haven't we, Toad?"

Toad nodded and pointed over the canal. "Yes, mateys, White Deer Park is thataway."

The Fair

It had been a very long, hard night. Everyone was tired. Fox was searching for a safe resting place for the Farthing Wood animals.

On a common he saw lots of tents and trailers. There were no humans around. "Come on, we'll be safe here," he said.

Fox led the animals between the tents of a travelling fair. He didn't know what a fair was, but it seemed a safe, quiet place.

Badger and Mole lifted up the flap of a big tent. "We'll stay here," said Mole. "I can't walk another step." Badger nodded.

One by one the animals found somewhere to curl up and rest. When Fox had seen them settled he lay down to sleep, too.

The fair was quiet all day, but in the late afternoon the humans who worked there started to appear. Bright lights were switched on.

Music woke Badger and Mole. It was very loud, and they blinked in surprise as bright lights lit up their resting place.

Mole cried out in alarm. "Look!" he said. "It's me, but it's not me." They were in the Hall of Mirrors, and Mole looked round and fat.

Badger looked tall and thin and wobbly in the middle. "Let's get out of here," said Badger, and they rushed out.

It was a sudden jolting movement that woke Adder. The soft seat where she had curled up swayed and rocked, then moved.

She looked out and gasped. She was right at the top of the big wheel ride, and the ground was a long, long way down.

Movement woke Toad and Weasel, too. "Wassat?" Toad cried as something wispy brushed against his face.

"Arrrgh!" cried Weasel as a shaking skeleton rattled against their resting place in the dark. They were on the ghost train ride.

"Whooooo!" said a ghost that leered out at them. "I'm getting out of here, matey," said Toad. Weasel was right behind him.

The fair was full of people now. Bright lights blazed and loud music played. At last Fox gathered everyone together.

"This is our first and last visit to a fair," he said. "Come on." The animals slipped into the darkness to continue their journey.

All about Moles

Moles are small animals about 15cm long. They have soft black fur and long pink noses called snouts. Because they spend most of their time underground in the dark they cannot see very well. They find their way around mainly by smell.

Moles are very strong. They live in tunnels in the earth which they dig with their wide front paws. They push the earth behind them using their back paws. Have you ever seen molehills made of this earth?

Moles need lots of food. Their favourite food is earthworms, but they also eat insects.

In the tunnels there is a nest for sleeping in, lined with bits of grass and leaves. There is a also a larder, where moles keep spare food until they need it.

Mole babies are born pink and helpless, but after about six weeks they have grown fur and are ready to go looking for food.

Weasel's Jokes

What should a bald rabbit wear?

A hare piece.

What do you call clever Owl?

Bird brain.

Which Farthing Wood animal is best at doing sums?

Adder.

What would you use to count a herd of cows?

A cowculator.

What do you call a camel with three humps?

Humphrey.

How can you tell the difference between a grape and an ape?

The grape is green.

What is Adder's favourite food?

Hisss fingers.

Which side of a sheep has the most wool?

The outside.

The Tip

A chill wind blew across the countryside. The leaves on trees and bushes were starting to turn brown. Berries and nuts replaced flowers and blossom. The days were getting shorter and the nights longer.

"I should be collecting nuts for my winter store now," said Squirrel. "And making my nest."

"I'm going to be ready for my winter sleep soon, too, matey," said Toad. "But we have to go on. Once we're at White Deer Park you'll have all the food and rest you need."

The animals reached an area of open ground that was bleak and empty.

There were no trees and bushes and no grass under their paws. A cold wind whistled around them and made them shiver.

"How much longer before we can rest, Fox?" asked a Fieldmouse.

"I don't know," said Fox. "Don't waste energy talking. Just keep walking."

Suddenly a big group of seagulls flew overhead. They dived and swooped around the animals. "Caaark!" said one of them. "You look a sorry lot. Haven't seen you in these parts before."

"We're just passing through," said Fox. "Heading for White Deer Park."

"That's a long way off," said the seagull.

"Yes, and we need to find food if we are going to get there," said Badger. "Is there any around here?"

"Plenty," said the seagull. "Follow me."

The seagull led the animals to the top of a small hill. They looked down into a dish-shaped hole that was full of steaming, smoking piles of rubbish. "This is home," said the seagull. "The tip. The humans throw lots of good stuff away and it ends up here."

The animals looked around hungrily. They could smell food. "Go on," said the seagull, "help yourselves. There's plenty for everyone."

Soon Fox and Vixen were gnawing on meaty bones, the Rabbits nibbled some cabbage leaves, and Badger chewed on a loaf of bread. The seagull was right – there was plenty of food for everyone.

"Caark!" said another gull. "Come and warm yourselves."

The Farthing Wood animals, tummies full for the first time in ages, settled down around a smouldering fire of burning rubbish. "Why not stay?" asked the seagull.

"It's tempting," said Badger, dozing off. "Very tempting..."

A few hours later, Mole and Fox woke up at the same time as the sky turned pale yellow and dawn broke over the tip. Their keen ears picked up faint sounds of rumbling and grumbling. "Sounds like thunder," said Fox. "Must be a storm coming."

But the noises got louder and louder, nearer and nearer. The seagulls were nowhere to be seen. Soon all the animals were awake. They felt uneasy. "That's no storm," said Badger.

He was right. Huge machines appeared on the ridge of the hill. They rumbled along on fat black tyres that brushed everything in their path. Big shovels on the front pushed piles of rubbish into the pit.

"Run for your lives!" cried Fox. "If we stay here we'll all be crushed or buried under that rubbish."

The animals scurried up the sides of the pit. The air was black with dust stirred up by the machines.

The animals stood in a frightened huddle
as Fox counted them. Someone was missing.

"It's Weasel," said Owl. "Where is she? Has
anyone seen her?"

The animals all shook their heads.

The roar and whine of the machines
seemed to be closing in on them. "Leave
her!" hissed Adder.

"We'll search for a few minutes, but if we
don't find her, we must go on," said Fox. "It's
too dangerous to stay."

39

The animals were searching when Mole held up his paw. His keen ears had picked up something. "Sssh. Listen."

The animals listened. Yes, it was a warbling, crying sort of sound. They followed it to an upturned metal bucket. The sound was muffled, but it was coming from inside.

Fox lifted up the bucket. "My old man's a dustman, he wears a dustman's hat, he wears..."

It was Weasel, singing to herself. She hadn't heard the noise of the machines inside the bucket.

The animals put their hands over their ears. "This is painful," said Mole.

Adder pulled a face. "Let'sss leave her here. Pleassse."

Fox smiled. "We'll take her with us," he said. "As long as she promises not to sing inside a bucket again. Come on."

The Worm Maze

The worm has a problem. He wants to get to the surface, but only one hole will take him there. Which one?

a   b   c   d   e   f

The answer is on page 61.

Thumb Print Animals

Make animal pictures using poster paints, felt-tip pens – and your thumbs!

Put some thick poster paint on an old saucer or plastic lid.

Put your thumb in the paint and press on to plain paper.

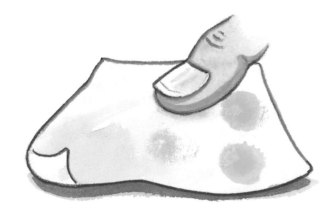

Use a felt-tip pen to draw on details like

ears,

faces,

tails

and legs.

Try spiders

a caterpillar

hedgehogs

or mice!

What other animals
can you make?

43

Danger!

The animals were walking beside a hedge when Mrs Hedgehog scurried up. "Stop, Fox, please stop!" she cried. "Help me!"

Fox held up his paw and everyone stopped. "It's Mr Hedgehog. His foot is caught in a nasty metal thing. We must go back for him."

"It's a nasty metal ring pull from a can of drink," said Vixen. Gently, she eased it off Mr Hedgehog's leg. It was very painful.

"Nasty thing," said Badger. "I wish humans would think about how dangerous their litter is for animals like us."

44

Vixen and Badger carried Mr Hedgehog back to the others. "One of my babies nearly died just now," said Mrs Rabbit.

"A plastic bag blew over her head and she couldn't breathe. I had to pull it off quickly. Those humans are so careless!"

The animals were about to set off again when Badger stopped. "Wait a minute, I've just seen something I need," he said.

It was a bit of a wooden lolly stick. "The perfect splint for Mr Hedgehog's leg," he said. "One bit of litter that IS useful!"

Animals in Hiding

Do you know what camouflage is?

It is the special colourings and markings that make animals hard to see. It helps them blend into the background.

Camouflage is useful for hunters who want to sneak up on their prey. It is also useful for animals who are hunted. If they stay very still their enemies may not see them.

The **puss moth** has markings that look just like the bark of trees. It can rest safely there without being seen.

When the **fallow deer** leaves her youngster to search for food its markings mean that it is almost invisible. As long as it stays quiet and still it will be safe.

Some animals can change their colour to match their surroundings. The **chameleon** is green when it is in a grassy place, brown when it is near rocks.

How many Farthing Wood
animals can you see?

Look carefully –
they are very well camouflaged.

The answers are on page 61.

49

Amazed

The animals were in the grounds of a big country house. "I can't remember which way to go," said Toad, scratching his head.

They heard the sound of yapping and loud barking. "The hounds," said Toad. "I remember them. We'll ask them the way."

There were about thirty hounds in a big pen. Fox and Vixen were scared. Hounds were used to hunt foxes.

"We could give this lot a run for their money, eh, lads?" said the biggest of the hounds, his red tongue lolling. The others barked and yapped.

Vixen and Badger carried Mr Hedgehog back to the others. "One of my babies nearly died just now," said Mrs Rabbit.

"A plastic bag blew over her head and she couldn't breathe. I had to pull it off quickly. Those humans are so careless!"

The animals were about to set off again when Badger stopped. "Wait a minute, I've just seen something I need," he said.

It was a bit of a wooden lolly stick. "The perfect splint for Mr Hedgehog's leg," he said. "One bit of litter that IS useful!"

All about Weasels

Weasels have long, slim bodies. Their fur is red-brown on top and yellowy-white underneath.

They can run very fast. Their bodies make a loop shape as they run, and they stop every now and then to stand on their back legs to look, listen and sniff around.

Weasels are good hunters. They go out mostly at night. They eat birds, birds' eggs, mice, voles, young rabbits and rats. They like to eat frogs, too, and will swim after them.

They make a nest of leaves, grass and moss in a hole or among tree roots. Baby weasels feed on their mother's milk until they are about four weeks old and can learn how to hunt.

Hidden Animals

Can you see some letters on flower petals and leaves?
Unscramble the letters to find the
names of five Farthing Wood animals.

Check your answers on page 61.

Animals in Hiding

Do you know what camouflage is?

It is the special colourings and markings that make animals hard to see. It helps them blend into the background.

Camouflage is useful for hunters who want to sneak up on their prey. It is also useful for animals who are hunted. If they stay very still their enemies may not see them.

The **puss moth** has markings that look just like the bark of trees. It can rest safely there without being seen.

When the **fallow deer** leaves her youngster to search for food its markings mean that it is almost invisible. As long as it stays quiet and still it will be safe.

Some animals can change their colour to match their surroundings. The **chameleon** is green when it is in a grassy place, brown when it is near rocks.

How many Farthing Wood
animals can you see?

Look carefully –
they are very well camouflaged.

The answers are on page 61.

Amazed

The animals were in the grounds of a big country house. "I can't remember which way to go," said Toad, scratching his head.

They heard the sound of yapping and loud barking. "The hounds," said Toad. "I remember them. We'll ask them the way."

There were about thirty hounds in a big pen. Fox and Vixen were scared. Hounds were used to hunt foxes.

"We could give this lot a run for their money, eh, lads?" said the biggest of the hounds, his red tongue lolling. The others barked and yapped.

50

Toad asked the way. "Just undo the bolt on this gate and we'll show you the way," said the hound. His big eyes glinted.

Fox's eyes flashed. "No, Toad, don't do that!" he said. "Don't even think about letting them out. They will kill us all!"

The hound smiled a cruel smile. "I'll still help you – even those tasty foxes," he said. "Go through the big green gates."

Inside the green gates the animals found themselves on a narrow path between high, green, very thick hedges. They set off.

The narrow path turned and twisted. "Right," said Toad. "No, ssstraight on," said Adder. Mole disagreed. "Turn left, I say."

The animals argued about which way to go. "This way," said Fox, and bumped into Badger. "No, dead end," he said.

The animals were lost in the maze. "I'll fly ahead," said Owl. "Follow me." But the animals could not keep up with her.

The animals had to get out before daybreak, when humans would come. Owl whispered something to Kestrel and they flew off together.

Owl and Kestrel were soon back with beaks full of shiny red rosehips and fat berries. They dropped some on the path.

"Kestrel and I will lay a trail of hips and berries to show you the way out," said Owl. "Just follow them, and stay together."

The animals all followed the trail. The Squirrels were the last ones out of the maze. Their arms were full of hips and berries.

One Squirrel took a big bite from a juicy rosehip. "Mmm, it tastes good," he said. "No use wasting good food, is there?"

All about Hares

Hares are bigger than rabbits. They have brown fur with white, orange and black hairs. This is good protection because it makes them difficult for enemies like eagles and foxes to see. If they are spotted, they run away very fast to escape, zigzagging from side to side.

Hares do not dig burrows. During the day they rest in hollows under hedges or in grassy banks. They come out at night to feed on root vegetables, cereal crops like wheat, and grass.

Baby hares are called leverets. They are born in grass-lined nests called forms. They feed on their mother's milk until they are ready to go looking for food when they are about three weeks old.

Male hares are called jacks, and females jills.

Nearly There...

Winter was coming fast. The trees were mostly bare now, their fallen leaves lying in rustling, crackling piles on the hard earth. An icy wind blew across the countryside.

As the animals set off one night, Badger walked along beside Fox and Vixen. "I'm worried," he said. "If we don't get to White Deer Park very soon, I don't think we ever will."

"I know," said Fox. "It's hard for all of us, but some of the small animals are getting very weak." He glanced back at the straggling line of animals. "Some of them, like Toad and Hedgehog, should be settling down for their long winter sleep soon. They won't be able to go on when the really cold weather comes."

"Perhaps Owl will bring us some good news," said Vixen. Owl had flown on ahead to see if she could find the nature reserve.

Next morning, as the animals settled down to rest for the day, many of them with empty tummies, Owl flew up on her silent wings. "I've seen it, I've seen it," she said. "I've seen White Deer Park."

"Thank goodness," said Fox. He turned to Badger. "Pass the word. Tell everyone. One more night's travelling, and we'll be at White Deer Park. Safe at last."

After what they all hoped would be their last long walk the animals reached the nature reserve, just as Toad had promised they would. But it was different.

Toad stopped at the foot of a high wire fence. "This 'ere fence is new, mateys," he said. He looked at the big animals. "I'm alright, shipmates, but you lot won't squeeze through these 'ere 'oles. Let's 'ope there's a gap somewhere for you lot to get through."

"We could dig under the fence, couldn't we, Moley?" said Badger.

Badger and Mole started to dig. But

the fence went deep under the ground and soon the earth was too stony to dig through. Badger and Mole had to give up.

"We have to find a way in," said Fox. "We haven't come all this way for nothing. There must be a way in." He turned to Vixen. "You run along the fence that way, and I'll go this way. One of us must find a way inside."

Fox was back first. He was panting hard. "No gaps that way," he gasped.

But Vixen had better news. "There's a big lake up that way. It's a sort of natural barrier and it isn't fenced. Let's try there."

Fox turned to the Fieldmice and the other small animals. "You go in here through the fence," he said. "We'll try the lake. If we get in we'll see you inside."

Toad stepped forward. "No, matey. We've come this far together, and we aren't going to jump ship now. It's all for one, and one for all, eh?"

The others all nodded.

The lake was broad and flat and looked very deep out in the middle. It was too far to the other side, even for the animals who could swim. Fox sat down. "Now what do we do?" It looked hopeless.

The animals all slumped to the ground. They were cold, tired and hungry. Inside the reserve was water, food and shelter. But they were outside...

58

Badger walked off on his own, head down, deep in thought. He flinched when his paw hit something hidden in the long grass.

A few minutes later he walked back to the others dragging two big black lids with him.

"What's that you've got?" asked Mole.

"The humans call them dustbin lids," Badger said, and floated one on the surface of the lake. "But I call them...boats!"

"You mean we could sail across?" asked Mole, and Badger nodded his wise old head.

The other animals crowded around and soon each dustbin lid boat was full of animals. Some friendly ducks helped to guide the boats with their beaks.

It took some time, but slowly, slowly, the boats sailed across the lake. As the sun came through the bare trees Badger stepped on to dry land again. "Welcome to White Deer Park," he said.

The animals stood and looked around.
They had been through hard times, danger
and adventure together.

Now they were safe in their new home.

Answers

page 15   Rabbits, Rabbits, Rabbits

Rabbits c and g are the same.

page 22   Farthing Wood Word Square

A	X	W	T	M	S	K	M	R	J
Y	H	E	D	G	E	H	O	G	N
V	B	V	U	H	L	I	L	Q	O
I	D	C	L	E	S	A	E	W	I
X	R	Z	V	K	R	J	G	H	P
E	E	A	K	E	S	T	R	E	L
N	D	U	G	F	L	D	R	P	W
E	D	D	F	X	T	S	A	O	O
W	A	E	B	C	D	M	F	O	X
B	G	H	A	R	E	Y	N	Q	T

page 41   The Worm Maze

Hole d leads to the surface.

page 47   Hidden Animals

1. Weasel, 2. Kestrel,
3. Vixen, 4. Badger, 5. Mole.

page 48   Animals in Hiding

Owl, Toad, Adder,
Hare and Mrs Pheasant
are hiding in the picture.

61